Learni

Bonface Fundafunda

Learning from the Hospitality Industry

LAP LAMBERT Academic Publishing

Imprint
Any brand names and product names mentioned in this book are subject to
trademark, brand or patent protection and are trademarks or registered
trademarks of their respective holders. The use of brand names, product
names, common names, trade names, product descriptions etc. even without
a particular marking in this work is in no way to be construed to mean that
such names may be regarded as unrestricted in respect of trademark and
brand protection legislation and could thus be used by anyone.

Cover image: www.ingimage.com

Publisher:
LAP LAMBERT Academic Publishing
is a trademark of
International Book Market Service Ltd., member of OmniScriptum Publishing
Group
17 Meldrum Street, Beau Bassin 71504, Mauritius

Printed at: see last page
ISBN: 978-613-9-96769-8

1. Introduction:

Public health sector facilities come under great scrutiny in terms of their performance, the conduct of their staff and the general working environment presented to the patient. These factors taken singularly or together, tend to shape public opinion about the quality of care, goods and service arising from the facility, but also shapes confidence in the health sector as whole. While great efforts have been made to addressed the service provision, the traditional approach of learning only from the health sector itself, have resulted in stagnation in terms of developing the health sector as a customer- facing, patient- focused member of the service industry, in tune with the absolute definition on hospital care or hospitality services. The health sector can learn much from the hospitality industry, by recognizing the common elements that apply to both health and hospitality services, given their common and historical background.

In the late 1990s, I was privileged to visit a public hospital somewhere in a Scandinavian country. The facility design and services available made one think that one was not visiting a public hospital, but some fancy, upmarket, colourful establishment. I recall there was a piano playing in the foyer, which itself was set up with flowers and had several little boutique shops. I was assured that the hospital was not a private hospital; it was public, paid for from tax-payers. The rest of the premises was just as colourful, spotless, not congested and inviting. The room I visited (I was visiting a family member of my host), was typically well- designed for light, peacefulness, comfort and healing.

I had just travelled from another African country which was had the typical high volume of patients attending the facility practically throughout the day. The hospital was as dramatic as one could imagine; these facilities were clearly not giving off quality, service and care. The message these facilities send to patients is one of a compromised health service. And it is no wonder that the quality of services is generally seen as compromised, when in fact so many health workers do their best to provide quality service, in spite of the overwhelming challenges that persist. Among the challenges are the difficulties in resource mobilization to meet the Abuja Declaration of health spending to be at minimum 15% of government budget (African Union, 2001; WHO, 2011). Faced with competing priorities, spending in the health sector is largely on securing the provision of the basic package of care, including provision of essential medicines and health supplies.

The health sector in most developing countries remains poorly financed, such that investing in a 'client- facing' service, is generally not a priority, even though healthcare provision is about providing a service to the patient. Between 2000 and 2015, donors reportedly spent over USD 200 billion on health sector services in low income countries (Institute of Health Metrics and Evaluation, 2015). This picture on spending, whether by developing countries themselves, or through donors, demands that effective solutions are found to 'make every penny count' in health sector services. The biggest challenge, it would seem, is in translating all this investment in health, into effective provision of quality health services, backed by effective management and administration structures.

The public health sector is a service- oriented sector, producing services that drive the health programmes in the country. These services are carried out by a variety of health professionals, from nurses to doctors; from accountants to supply chain specialists. This human resource provides all manner of specialized medical and supporting services. This human resource needs to be consistently strengthened for it to provide sustained quality services. There is room within capacity building strategies, to revisit the strategies for building or strengthening the capacity of that human resource. In many cases, the sector carries out human resource capacity building as an intra- sector activity, using the same training approach of workshops, seminars and so forth; the same managers of health programmes and technical areas may be the providers of the capacity-building programme, or other external agents are contracted to provide the training services. Capacity is defined as "..the ability of individuals and organizations or organizational units to perform functions effectively, efficiently and sustainably. Capacity building is an evidence-driven process of strengthening the abilities of individuals, organizations, and systems to perform core functions sustainably, and to continue to improve and develop over time' (UNDP, 2008).

The greatest challenge with the traditional HR capacity building approach is in translating the workshop or classroom training into practice. The repetitive training of the same staff in the same subject area at the same level suggests, at least, a problem in translating training into achievement on the job. The health sector programmes tend to have stringent clinical programme monitoring framework which has served health sector well. This includes monitoring framework for successful translation of training into effective and positive outputs on management of services. But the rate of success in HR capacity building for services, appears low, suggesting low impact from traditional human resource training approach. In studying the Local Government Reform Programme (LGRP) of Tanzania, in which Human Resource Development (HRD), Organization Development (OD), and Institutional Development (ID) dimensions were considered, Pallangoyo and Reese (2010) found that "in relation to both HRD and OD, the LGRP resulted in positive impacts but had failed to address critical deficiencies such as poor training coordination, the inability to attract and retain skilled employees, and unsatisfactory working conditions. The ID dimension of the study identified the continued existence and application of old labour laws, a lack of fiscal autonomy at LGA level, contradictory policies, political interferences and donor dependence". While this paper is not going to attempt to address factors such as political interference, this situation described by the above authors, begs for a different approach to human resource capacity building.

Dada, J.O. presents critical statement on the nature of HR in many institutions of the developing countries, which is worth reading. He describes the state of the public services in the African public sector as "..oppressive, unjust, imposing, non-existent, unproductive and inefficient… as a clog in the wheel of progress. It has indeed been described as prostrate and inefficient... Viewed from this perspective, Africa public service delivery mechanism has failed – albeit woefully". In the same article, Dada states that "The primacy of the customer dictates that it provides services that are responsive to the needs of its primary customer - the public. The main objective of a customer-focused approach is to improve service delivery and is characterized by consulting users of services, setting services standard (s), increasing access, ensuring courtesy, providing more useful information, increasing openness and transparency, preventing mistakes and failures (and ensuring timely correction when they occur), providing the best value for money, enhanced accountability. Encouraging innovation, rewarding excellence and building partnerships with the wider community". Capacity building or capacity strengthening in the public sector, is a not an easy activity, whether this is done for an institution or the individual.

There are simply too many factors that are required to be considered, including how well invested in this process, the service providers are. Van der Werf (2007) has collected various definitions of capacity building / strengthening and points to the very challenging narrative, design of work, implementation and most importantly, evaluation of results and to attribution and associations that accompanies this area of work. Thus, one is bound to look at other approaches that might enhance the investment in capacity building activities in developing countries. Along the same vein, Prashanth et al (2014), also give an attempt at how best to develop a capacity building programme that would have impact; their approach was to develop a "program theory to understand how such a capacity-building program could bring about organizational change. A well-formulated program theory enables an understanding of how interventions could bring about improvements and an evaluation of the intervention. In the refined program theory of the intervention, we identified various factors at individual, institutional, and environmental levels that could interact with the hypothesized mechanisms of organizational change, such as staff's perceived self-efficacy and commitment to their organizations". Crisp, et al (2000) also present a refreshing view of how the health sector has approached capacity building in recent times. They argue that "..capacity building has its roots in a range of disciplines which in the 1970s flew the flag for empowerment, e.g. community development, international aid and development, public health and education. Although these traditions are somewhat inter-related and have, to varying degrees, been concerned with developing healthy communities, it is perhaps not surprising that 'capacity building' as a term has been conceptualized in a diverse range of ways and associated with a plethora of meanings", and proceed to describe approaches to capacity building in the health sector. Among the approaches they have discussed, is a partnership strategy between the health sector and other non- health sector entities, where lessons can be gained.

In short, capacity building is a necessary part of development programme implementation, because of the positive impact it can have in enabling institutions to achieve their targets. The approaches may be numerous, but there is no one magic strategy that will provide guarantee to achieving the ideal result. Therefore, the sector has to strive to consistently consider strategies that will provide effective capacity building results, and directly result in positive impacts on programmes in the public arena.

At a local level, it should be possible for the health sector to learn from other service-oriented and evidently more successful sectors, such as the hospitality industry, with which the health sector shares a lot in common. In learning from others, the health sector can get practical lessons in translating sector or institutional policies, strategies into actions on their health programmes, that result in sustained and positive benefits and outcomes to the patient and the health sector as a whole. Every aspect of the health sector can learn from others. In particular, the procurement and supply chain service for health is a critical element of health services, as it requires to make health commodities available at every service delivery point throughout the year.

2.   Common elements between health and hospitality industry

Why choose the hospitality industry? The term 'hospitality' is defined by most dictionaries, as 'the friendly and generous reception and entertainment of guests, visitors, or strangers'. The terms 'hospitality' and 'hospital' share the same origin or etymology (Wikipedia). The hospitality industry provides services to visiting guests who use its services such as restaurants, rooms, and other facilities. The industry offers goods and services that the industry has to procure or create in-house and provide these to the guest. The health sector provides services to patients, and as part of the services, has to procure goods and services. Both the health and hospitality sectors must comply with laws and regulations that govern how goods and related services for health, are procured, stored, supplied and used by or on the patient, as shown in Table 1. Service to the guest at any hospitality facility across the world is based on quality and implementation of business and operational policies and strategies, and industry- related laws, rules and regulations. The hospitality industry has unequalled commitment to ensuring that the client receives the best service they can offer, to ensure that the guest has the best experience, and to make that guest return in future, or tell others about their experience. Further, the hospitality industry is subject to critical peer and guest opinion about goods and services, that industry players have to respond to in order to remain the business (see Lonely Planet). Similarly, hospitals are mindful of providing quality services to the patient, as the purpose of the hospital is to treat and heal the infirm. It would not serve the health sector well, if services were such that no treatment or healing took place.

Table 1: Some common services between hospitality industry and hospital services

Quantification and forecasting
Budgeting and financing
Establishing sources of quality goods and services
Pre- qualification of sources of goods and services
Procurement and Contracting strategies
Logistics strategies
Cold chain services
Waste Management
Human Resource management and capacity development
Compliance to industry and national laws and regulations (food, health and safety, etc)

Thus, the setting up of policies and strategies in the health sector, helps to drive the sector to be a provider of quality assured services that comply to all laws, rules and regulations, for the benefit of the patient, and therefore the country. Table 2 shows operational similarities between the hospital and the hotel.

3.   **Classification of hotels and restaurants**

Rating services are a well- established service to governments, industries, corporations and to individuals. They aim to provide objective assessment of a government or corporate or an individual against common factors that will help investors, shareholders, potential employers or users of goods and services, to make an informed decision on whether to invest (with expectation of high-returns) or to employ or to procure a service (with profitable outcome). Hotel, lodges, cafes and restaurants are generally classified on the presence or availability of specific services and facilities that they offers to the guest (see Hotel ratings at Wikipedia). Thus, hotels can be classified as 1, 2, 3, 4 and 5 star facilities (see Hotel Stars); these ratings speak also about the quality of service that the guest can expect to find at these establishments (see Tourism). The hotel rating system and standards are applicable across the hospitality industry and across the world, as the parameters on which ratings are based, are the same since all aspects of a hotel service are being judged and compared among the hotels. Clearly, it is important to be rated as that adds value to the hotel business.

Table 2: Similarity in hospital and hotel service

TARGET	HOSPITAL	HOTEL
Client	Person for treatment	Person is on holiday
Stay	Admission for treatment	Short- to- long stay
Meals	Served, to the bed	Dining, in-house restaurants
Procurement	Medicines, foods	Foods, beverages, entertainment material
Logistics	Yes	Yes
Cold Chain	Yes	Yes
Transportation	Yes	Yes
Waste Management	Yes	Yes
Compliance to laws and regulations	For medicines, medical devices; health and safety, services	Foods, beverages, entertainment, health and safety;
Personnel service providers	Doctors, nurses, pharmacists, cleaners, store keepers, maintenance	Chef, waiters, valets, front desk, store keepers, cleaners, maintenance
Management	Administration, finance, HR	Administration, finance, HR
Quality Assurance	Yes, goods and services	Yes, goods and services

Hotels then strive to retain or improve upon the rating level as that has direct relation with the level of profitability. Across the world, the hospitality industry is a well recognized contributor to national development (Australian Hotels Association, 2013; American Hotels and Lodging; Morissete, 2013; World Travel and Tourism, 2017). In the majority of developing countries, there are good hospitality industry players, and these include hotels and restaurant whose services are internationally recognized.

4. What drives Quality Assurance in the Hospitality Industry

Hotels largely exist and prosper through differentiation of each establishment and what it offers the paying client, with a view to make that client to keep returning to that establishment. Differentiation will apply to the physical infrastructure, the uniqueness of what is offered in terms of goods and services.

Other management decisions also help to make the hotel to continue being viable. For example, as stated by Samsuddin (2013), hotels can cut operational costs to keep being viable. However, the quality and impact of their services certainly relies on putting in place an effective and efficient, quality assured procurement and supply chain management. As stated by Nicolaides and Peristeris, (2011), "...The aim of logistics is to satisfy the needs of customers. Business logistics contributes to an organisation's success by providing customers with timely and accurate product delivery". It is this element that the health sector needs to learn from the hospitality industry and apply in the provision of healthcare services, particularly procurement and supply chain services.

5.   **Classification of public health facilities**

The rating system that has so helped and driven the hospitality industry is not applied to the public health services infrastructure, certainly in the developing country context, even though the spirit behind the rating initiative can be used to drive the establishment and provision of all services in the public health sector. In some countries, 'world- class' healthcare facilities have been set up to rival hotels in almost all aspects of customer services. Indeed, these health facilities are heavily invested in, are generally private, and are found in high income countries; the health facilities will have management and administration infrastructure that can easily compare with the best in the hospitality industry (see Dubai Hospitals and Health Centres). If one was to consider taking the same approach to reform the public health sector management and service provision, one could start with application of such improvements at the different levels of the healthcare service infrastructure. Public hospitals in many developing countries are generally classified according to the level of care that they are set up to provide, as either primary or tertiary care (Uganda Ministry of Health, 2015; WHO, 2006). Generally, public health services in developing countries will be structured as follows:

   i.   The main national referral hospital, that provides more sophisticated range of health services to patients referred from the provincial hospitals (tertiary care)
   ii. The provincial or state referral hospital, that provides a broad package of care to patients referred from district hospitals. This facility can also be referred to provide tertiary care

iii. The district hospital, to provide a broad package of care, including surgery, to patients referred from health centres (can offer primary and some tertiary care)
iv. The health centre, to provide basic primary care to patient referred from health posts
v. The health post, to provide basic primary health care to a set number of people in a district
vi. The community health worker, to provide basic primary health care to a set number of people in a community

The public health facilities may further be classified on the basis of number of beds they have for admissions, which translates into the type of healthcare services these facilities will offer, or the required clinical services to be offered by health facilities in that country (Sternberg, 2016).

6.   Quality of Care and Service

Hospitals are primarily service providers to the patient and the general public as a whole, and in that regard, it is to be expected that the users or receivers of the services will have certain expectations on the quality and effectiveness of the services. Across many developing countries, the quality of health care services from public sector health facilities is determined by the quality of the hospital infrastructure (working environment), the quality of management, and indeed the attitude of the healthcare staff towards the patient. All these and other factors taken together send a message of quality of services to be expected from these public sector facilities. In a detailed study on this subject, Al Damen (2017) tested various variables (Reliability, Assurance, Tangibles, Responsiveness, and Empathy) determining patient satisfaction with healthcare services at one Jordanian government hospital. In this regard, the author concluded that "that perceived overall patient satisfaction was in medium category. Patients were moderately satisfied with the medical, nursing and management services provided in the hospital", and that there were no differences in patient perceptions of health service quality dimensions attributed to any of the demographic variables (gender, age, education, income and residence)". This is an important finding: That it does not matter the age, gender, education or income level or indeed the residence of the patient; the minimum expectation on what is quality service, is the same. Similar findings by other researchers have been observed, for example, as observed by Singh

(2010) who reported various areas of dissatisfaction in service provision at several government hospitals in Haryana State of India.

The absence of quality assured healthcare services often results in investors and other local or international businesses, having to invest in creating their own healthcare facilities (in some cases, including education establishments) to look after the health of their staff and their families (see First Quantum, 2013 and International Council on Mining and Metals, 2013).

7.   National Quality Assurance Policies

Many developing countries have recognized the importance of instituting a quality assurance policy in their public sector services. Quality assurance in service provision aims to ensure that in terms of goods and services, these outputs are of a high quality at all times, being provided by personnel that are trained to focus on quality, using training programmes in which quality is intrinsically imbedded. Thus, we see many countries setting up their national quality assurance policy that either direct the whole country to apply and meet the minimum national quality standards for goods and services (Zambia Ministry of Commerce, Trade and Industry, 2011). At a global level, multi-lateral organisations such as COMESA (2009) and UNIDO (2016), are promoting the setting up of national quality assurance policies, ensure that goods and services meet the standard expected. To be competitive, even in a community such as the COMESA group of countries, countries must ensure that their policies, laws, strategies and regulations for goods and service in both public and private sectors, are founded on quality. At institutional level, this national quality assurance policy should be translated into an implementation or activity plan in all sectors. Interestingly, the hospitality industry had always been ahead in this respect, and has over the years gained experience in applying quality in all aspects of its goods and services.

8.   Quality Assurance in Healthcare services

Governments across the world are committed to provision of quality assured goods and services that are provided to the patient (WHO, 2003). There are also efforts to improve the quality of the working environment, the quality of institutional management team, institutional and service administration, as much as clinical and support services are routinely improved. However, while infrastructure can be constructed, and operational tools and other material goods can be procured and deployed, the creation of quality performance and therefore the change in staff approach to service per se, is the more challenging area.

Many developing countries continue to invest in the development and strengthening of their health sectors. They do this by ensuring that there are strategies and systems that enable them to access medicines and other health commodities. Further, they have invested in the development of laws, policies, strategies, regulations and implementation plans for effective provision of health services and health products to their people. There is also investment in development of human resources for health, as pointed out above. The objective in such investments, is quite often efficiency and the term is used in conjunction with quality of goods and services offered to the patient, and rightly so. Further still, in a world of increasing demands on the health sector services, competing demand on finite resources, governments have seen the value of integrating planning and service provision, to make the best use of the limited resources that they have. To ensure that each level and type of investment achieves its intended objective, operational systems call for establishment of standards, procedures,

benchmarks, oversight, supervision, and undertaking corrective measures when faults are found. This approach in its totality, is describing the building of quality within each task, job and function, and therefore in all areas for work for which one is responsible and accountable for. The public health sector is awash with capacity building / strengthening workshops in many aspects of services it provides. These programmes include capacity building activities in clinical services, planning, management, monitoring, supervision, reporting, etc. It would appear that the missing link is the lack of developing a specific Quality Assurance policy and implementation plan that would enable the health sector to transform into a provider of customer- centric services. This is what governments are now doing: following on from the COMESA advocacy that countries must imbed quality in all aspects of their services and goods, this has been taken up to create sector quality assurance policies (for example, Botswana, 2015) and as seen in the health sector quality assurance policies on health in general, and specifically in respect to medicines and other health products (for example, Nigeria, 2015).

9.   **Building Quality in goods and services**

Building quality in goods and services is also about transforming people, about how we define quality and also about what we should or should not accept about the state of goods and services. One person's definition of quality is different from another person. The national quality assurance is for the whole country, addressing all affairs in the public and private sectors. In developing a national quality assurance framework, it is important to start from education stage, which should mean that from primary education to undergraduate years, the education process (curriculum, teach and learning experience) must be built on quality and that this must continue into the postgraduate and practice years. Institutions then translate the national quality standards into their institutional quality policy which sets the institutional quality standards on products and services, which goes to define the standard operating procedures, job descriptions, management, supervision, monitoring, evaluation, training, etc. That way, quality is built into the organisation and this approach defines the quality that can be repeated each time a product is made or a service is offered to a client.

This national quality assurance policy and implementation framework is applicable to all players in the sector, from decision-makers to different stakeholders. The national quality assurance policy provides intent and direction in regards to how the state wishes to see services and goods provided and managed. The national quality policy identifies the stakeholders associated with provision and / or use of pharmaceutical and other health products and their responsibilities in implementation of the NQAP

9.1. Identification of Stakeholders in Health Sector

In many countries, the health sector is structured in such a way that the stakeholders are well known. These include the policy and strategy makers (eg, MOH), the regulators (regulating practice and goods), the implementers (eg, public and private health facilities, the overseers / supervisors at central, state and district levels), the associated providers of key goods and services (eg, manufacturing, importation, procurement, warehousing, distribution/ transportation, communication, etc). This also includes the related professional bodies that enhance professionalism and adherence and compliance to regulations and professional standards. It is these stakeholders that are responsible for ensuring that the defined standards for quality assurance in these areas of work are being applied.

9.2. Defining Quality Standards in public health

The stakeholders have the key responsibility of defining what the quality standards are for each area of professional and associated services. Even in this process, the country and sector has to recognize that the purpose of creating quality standards to assure that goods and services that are being used on the patient are of a quality that, when used correctly, will result in positive outcome for the patient. This position does not only apply to goods (medicines, medical supplies), but to services, such as diagnosis process, advice and instruction to the patient; laboratory and rapid test service; manufacturing, importation, procurement, warehousing, transportation, storage, management and communication of stock. International standards are available for practically any level of service or goods. It is the responsibilities of the stakeholders to define and develop the standards that are to apply in that sector, bearing in mind that these standards must meet internationally accepted standards for goods and services.

9.3. Quality Assurance and Regulations

It is important to appreciate that creating quality in all aspects of services, production of goods and provision of those goods, cannot arise purely from enforcing regulations. The evidence that exists in any country about the level of poor compliance to regulations, misinterpretation of regulations, demonstrate that the underpinning quality foundation is weak in the way the stakeholders are developed in those problem areas. Quality assurance policy sets the direction where the country is going in respect to goods and services. Quality assurance also sets the highest threshold in terms of goods and services. The intention is to ensure that the practitioners are at one with regulations, as these regulations arise from quality assurance policy. To that end, the practitioners can ensure that in all aspects of their professional service, they ensure that compliance to set quality standards, and therefore compliance to rules and regulations, is part and parcel of their existence, and not a secondary thought. Therefore, such a situation should make regulatory services less of a punitive step and more constructive process. It follows therefore, that the stakeholders defining quality standards on practice have to ensure that part of that process is to ensure that the student is well educated in applicable laws, policies, rules and regulations that apply to the profession. It is important to ensure that the process of education does not leave out this component, as later the person so poorly trained will at best misinterpret the rules and regulations, or worse argue with and challenge the rules, regulations, with the result the cost of enforcement of regulations would forever be high.

9.4. Quality Assurance in Education Process

The goal of the national quality assurance framework in respect to education process for health professionals is to ensure that the education process is imbedded with quality in terms of the course content, the teaching resources, and those that are educators. That is, quality is built into the education process. The education infrastructure is then stringently regulated to ensure that any registered and accredited training institution is delivering quality education that meets international standards. In order to create and sustain the quality of education, all centres of high education where pharmacists are trained, will consider the aspirations of the NQAP for provision of quality services in pharmaceutical practice and practices related to the use of other health products. The education process is accompanied by an internship period when the graduate undergoes practice period when they are presented with the reality of providing services in their professional area. This internship period can make or break a profession, if quality is not imbedded in the process.

9.5. Quality Assurance in Professional development

Professional bodies either are associations of members of that profession, or they are also regulatory institutions that regulate the profession. In either case, the professional bodies, as stakeholders, have one interest, which is to ensure that their members apply themselves in line with the quality standards set for professional practice, and the provision of goods and services. However, the professional body has an interest in the structure of the education framework and practice for those going to join the profession, ensuring that the whole is founded on quality standards and compliance to rules and regulations. The professional body cannot leave this foundational part to academia alone. Therefore, the structure and content of the undergraduate, internship and postgraduate CPD or specialization programmes, must meet the minimum professional practice standards set by the professional body.

9.6. Quality Assurance in the Procurement and Supply Chain Services

In this context, procurement and supply chain services are being considered to include manufacturing, procurement, warehousing, storage at facilities, provision of medicines to the patient at health facilities and pharmacies.

9.6.1. Manufacturing

Pharmaceutical manufacturing is a highly complex and demanding process. The guidance provided by WHO on Good Manufacturing Practice (2011) provides minimum requirements in terms of standards, resources and processes that must be invested in. It is not an area of industry or commerce that one can enter into without a commitment to entertain high investment in human and material resources. The manufacturer's responsibilities lies in translating national quality standards into business quality policies and operational standards, and to ensure that all its human resources are sufficiently trained as to apply those standards. Standards exist for practically every aspect of the manufacturing step.

9.6.2. Procurement Service

Any entity that is carrying out procurement of medicines and other health products, will be required to demonstrate good practice, by way of compliance to firstly, laws and regulations underpinning public procurement. Secondly, they will do so in order to comply with rules and regulations pertaining to procurement and supply for human or animal use, any medicines and other health products. Quality assurance therefore needs to be imbedded in the procurement processes, to ensure that only quality health commodities are procured every time. The institution will develop an institutional quality assurance policy based on the national quality assurance policy. More often than not, countries are pre- qualifying manufacturers and suppliers of medicines and medical supplies, as a way of protecting and safeguarding public health and welfare. Therefore, it is of great advantage when the procurement team consist of staff that are also well versed in medicines regulations, supply and storage. Procurement entities can set up procurement policy in which is imbedded quality assurance. Such a policy will, as a minimum, contain the following commitments:

i. Application of Good Procurement Practice as imbedded in national procurement laws and regulations (ZPPA, 2008 & Regulations, 2011), and including application of procurement rules and regulations from bilateral and multilateral financing agencies (Gabra, 2006; Global Fund, 2009)

ii. Procurement of pharmaceutical and other health products listed in the National Essential Medicines List, which are duly registered in the country

iii. Pre- qualification of manufacturers and other sources of pharmaceutical and other health products, to assure quality, safety and efficacy of medicines and other health products. Pre- qualification of manufacturers and suppliers of pharmaceutical and other health products enables the buyer to determine and control the source of all health products, ensuring that all processes from manufacture to delivery of health commodities are performed in accordance to nationally established and standards. In this process, the procuring entity need to invest in working with the national medicines regulatory authority, which at national level, is a partner to the national procuring entity

iv. Taking into consideration recommendations on procurement of medicines and other health products as regularly presented by institutions such as WHO, UNICEF and from those countries with stringent medicines regulatory authorities

v. Procurement of the right medicines and other health products in the right quantities and at the right price

vi. Transparency in procurement processes and decisions

vii. Documentation and record keeping of all processes, events, etc, that occur in each contract

viii. Stringent management of any third-party procurement services that might be set up

ix. Fiduciary discipline in procurement, ensuring that medicines budget are used effectively

x. Invest in developing quality HR across the procurement and supply chain institutions, through recruitment of qualified, experienced staff, and provision of capacity building, including continuous professional development for staff

9.7. Quality Assurance and Quality Control of medicines and Health Supplies

The purpose of the receiving function is to ensure that the arriving consignment is correct, that such products originate from approved suppliers and that products have not been visibly damaged during transport. To provide assurance of the quality status of the consignment, the policy and SOPs should include the following tasks:

i. Incoming consignments should be examined to verify the integrity of the container/closure system, ensure that tamper-evident packaging features are intact

ii. Temperature condition monitoring devices have not been compromised

iii. Labelling is intact

iv. Products have not been damaged during transport. Samples of products received are then taken for quality control to check conformity with applicable standards.

9.8. Warehousing and Distribution services

Warehousing and distribution of medicines and other health products is an integral part of the procurement and supply chain service. Quality assurance in each of the steps involved, from receipt of goods to the delivery at the health facility. The World Health Organisation's Good Distribution Practice guidelines (2011), and similar guidelines from the European Union (2013) are available and are based on ensuring that quality is imbedded into these steps.

9.9. Management of medicines and health supplies in the supply chain

Good practice in management of medicines and other health products is a starting point for building quality in the goods and related services. These products require stringent managing by way of application of regulations and management practices for health commodities. These principles apply to products in use, or when these products are expired and are being prepared for destruction. At the central medical stores, many of these institutions have recognized the importance of installing intelligent resource management tools that provide information to management on the stock status, movement of stock in the pipeline, cost of services, among other functions. These Enterprise Resource Planning (ERP) tools enable quality in system management to be available that results in quality, evidence- based decision- making (Muscatello and Chen, 2010).

9.9.1. Dispensing Medicines in Patients Packs

Dispensing of medicines in patient packs designed to carry all the legal and regulatory requirements on a package, and containing a patient leaflet, preserves and enhances the quality of pharmaceutical service. The use of patient packs for dispensing of fixed number of treatment forms, has been accompanied by controversy primarily in respect to the limitations imposed on the prescriber (Buisson, 2003). Generally, the prescriber determines the treatment to be given to the patient, and that treatment can require a certain number of treatment forms (tablets, capsules, etc) to be in that treatment package, for the stated number of treatment days. However, a fixed treatment package as presented by a patient pack of the stated number of treatments, suggests a limitation or restriction on the treatment period. Patient packs are in fact based on the internationally accepted treatment period for a given, basic condition, and these treatment protocols are generally covered in national Standard Treatment Guideline (STGs). However, the STGs promote the rational and correct use of medicines, without restricting the prescriber from providing the correct treatment to a patient, that may require dispensing of more medicines to the patient.

In many countries, the use of patient packs is now routine following years of argument about this strategy (East Cheshire NHS Trust, 2017), and some developing countries have applied this concept (MOH Malaysia, 2008) However, most developing countries were planning for and procured bulk packed supplies of pharmaceutical products for use in the public health sector. The argument has been that these bulk packs were cheaper to procure and use for the large populations served in the public health system. On the other hand, the private community pharmacies have traditionally procured patient- pack sizes for most pharmaceutical products, were this is done as a matter of norm. However, the use of patient pack sizes has not generally been considered as applicable in the public health environment, because:

i. Generally, the sector is targeting to treat thousands of patients in any one year

ii. The prescriber may prescribe more medicines, or less than that presented in the patient pack size, based on clinical diagnosis

iii. The bulk pack allows for ease of dispensing diverse number of tablets, capsules or volumes of liquid medicines to patients with different degrees of illness, as directed by the prescriber

iv. It is considered cheaper to supply a pack of 100s, 500s, or 1,000s tablets as bulk, from which to dispense the required number of tablets per patient, than a patient pack

v. A standard pack size of a treatment as too prescriptive for the prescriber, in terms of how many of that treatment tablets, capsules or the volume of the liquid to dispense.

The same argument has been applied to oral liquid forms, where large volume (eg, 1, 2, 2.5 and 5 litre) containers were procured from which small volume packs (25ml, 50ml, 100ml, 250ml) would be dispensed. For liquid oral forms, the argument was also that procuring patient 'liquid' packs (50, 100ml, etc) is equally expensive, as opposed to procuring and distributing fewer, large volume packs. Additionally, it was considered cheaper to procure and supply empty dispensing bottles for small pack dispensing to the patient at the health facility.

9.9.2. **Application of standard pack sizes**

The use of patient packs in the supply chain presents a number of advantages in management of the logistics of the stock. In combination with the use of electronic stock management systems, the patient pack with its own bar code, enables better stock management of medicines. The electronic stock supply and management system that can apply itself to the patient pack, is the same as the same commercial point of sell (POS) system that is used in retail outlets for the sell and accounting of many products. The integrated PSO system registers each sell and the system will provide all the information to the vendor on how many units of that product have been sold, and what is remaining in stock. The system can also be predictive, to the extent that it can estimate what additional stock of that product needs to be brought into the stock at the retail outlet, to prevent a stock- out situation. In retail outlets where a POS system is applied, we see that the primary vendor will also have the responsibility to ensure that their product is on the shelves in that retail outlet. Occasionally, it is the product license holder (or the primary vendor) who, in agreement with the retail outlet owner, ensures that the product is on the shelves of that retail outlet every day:

i.   The vendor supplies their product to the retail outlet

ii.   The retail outlet may have allocated a specific space on the shelves for that product.

iii. The vendor will routinely monitor the state of their stock at the retail outlet, to ensure that the outlet has sufficient stock in store room and on their shelves to meet demand from the customer. This is a vendor-managed inventory (VMI) service

iv.   The vendor may be linked to the retail outlet via the electronic POS system, which allows the vendor remote access to data on the stock status and sells of their product at the retail outlet, allowing the vendor to have real- time information on the stock status and sells, and from that data, to have ability to plan for future business

Any product of whatever description, can be managed in real- time using the VMI principle. In a similar way, the central medical stores can manage its services to the health facilities using both VMI and 'POS' type of electronic stock management systems that provide real- time capabilities.

9.10. Management of Patient Packs

Patient packs of medicines are well designed to be managed in this way, allowing for a high level of accuracy in stock management, planning, forecasting, quantification and budgeting. The large containers will not provide for the efficiency that patients packs provide, as additional manipulation of quantities of tablets actually dispensed, will be required.

Patient packs present an efficient way of stock management and collecting data on medicines consumption, up to the level of the tablet or capsule or millilitre of liquid dispensed. For example, using electronic stock management systems, when the health facility consignment is delivered to the health facility, this consignment can be scanned into the health facility stores. At that point, the at the health facility is updated, and that information is immediately sent to the central warehouse at NMSF. Thereafter, using electronic stock management systems:

i. When stock is required to move to the Dispensary, the pharmacist will scan out of the Store Room an estimated quantity of all the medicines for dispensing that day
ii. The stock in the Store Room and Dispensary is automatically updated
iii. With a link to the central medical stores, there is real- time access to information on the stock status and movement at that health facility wherever it is located in the country.

9.10.1. Linking patient packs and electronic prescription

Another process that the patient pack medicines can contribute to, is in obtain accurate data on stock of medicines that where prescribed and dispensed (or sort of balance sheet on medicines usage at the health facility). This would work well in real- time, when the prescriber is provided with a facility to issue an electronic prescription (e-prescription) system that is linked directly to the pharmacy. In that way, therefore:

i. When the pharmacy receives the e-prescription the pharmacists prepares the prescription

ii. Additional / special instruction to the patient can be prepared and printed on a special label

iii. The patient pack is scanned out of the Dispensary and presented to the patient with the usual verbal instruction on how to use the product

iv. The stock status in the Dispensary and in the Store room at the health facility, is updated

v. Because the dispensary is linked to the health facility's stock database, the data held at the central medical stores, is also automatically updated.

vi. The central medical stores system (ie, the Enterprise Resource Planning tool, or ERP where such are installed) immediately starts to prepare a replenishment consignment to be delivered to that health facility at the appropriate date, to avoid a stock out.

In this set up, the electronic prescription systems is linked or integrated to the health facility electronic stock management system. With that set up, therefore, accurate stock movement and medicines consumption data can be generated and reported on a regularly basis (hourly, daily, weekly, monthly, etc). Further, this information can be more reliable as true picture of actual consumption of medicines at that health facility, allowing for a more accurate data for planning, forecasting, quantification, budgeting, trend analysis and analysis against a range of factors that can influence consumption rates.

These operating systems provide for quality of work at the central medical stores and all the way up to the service delivery point.

9.11.   Stock Management strategies and Communication tools

There is a distinct difference between advertising health services, which in most countries (for example, Australia, 2011) is restricted, and communicating and promoting health services. In many developing countries, the health sector is not known for effective and efficient communication. As indicated above, dialogue between a patient and a caregiver is generally difficult, when patients appear to be intimidated by the institution and professionals, and when professionals are under pressure to move patients along. It becomes challenging to explain processes, let alone provide advice to patients on what to expect from medicines dispensed, etc. In some cases, as seen above, patients feel they cannot demand on the doctor, as after all, the doctor is doing all he/ she can for that patient. Ways have to be found to serve the patient in a manner that allows for constructive dialogue between the service provider and the patient. Increasingly, however, institutions and operational supply chain systems are investing in the use of real- time communication tools. This is enabling in some cases, to integrate stock management, ordering and reporting between offices within the supply chain. In Zambia, the application of real- time stock management and communication systems called the Electronic Zambia Inventory Control System (e-ZICS) is helping to provide real-time reports on the status of stock along the supply chain (Leung, N-H, Z., et al, 2015). Through a scanning facility, this tool collects data on stock receipts and movement from between store rooms and up to the dispensary and to the patient. For example, from any place in the world, an authorized user can view stock status at any health facility. This tool communicates data and information on stock in a cost- effective way, and allows decision makers to have access accurate data in real- time. This results in securing the quality of data and therefore the quality of work, providing assurances to clinical services.

10. A national policy for the private health sector

The relationship between the private health sector and public health sector is often fraught with misunderstanding and a loss of opportunity to create partnerships and provision of quality services to the public. This is in spite of the fact that the national development plans of many developing countries in Africa, articulate so well the intention of governments to work with private sector on national development projects, and for private sector to be providers of goods and services. And yet, in practice, this intention is not generally applied beyond expectation that the private sector will offer price discounts for goods and services procured, etc.

The Miltonian (1970) view of the private sector, as only focused in returning a profit to its shareholders, had contributed to the view that the private health sector cannot be relied upon to have a pure public service intent. Nonetheless, this view notwithstanding, many governments have recognized that as a state, they can enable the private sector to indeed have a profitable occupation and at the same time provide an acceptable service to the patient in particular, and to the general public as a whole. For example, the Sudan Federal Ministry of Health (FMOH, 2009) in Sudan published a National Policy for Private 'for profit' Health Sector. In this Policy, the FMOH stated that the Government "..places a high level of importance to the private health sector in the provision of much needed health services to the people of Sudan. They are a key pillar of the health system and contribute significantly to the overall social and economic development of the country... health, which being central to the human development, is a social and human right of all citizens of Sudan, irrespective of their regional, religious, racial, cultural or ethnic affiliation. In this endeavour, the private 'for profit' health sector is an important partner and government shall harness its capacity in a meaningful manner... It is essentially a win-win strategy in order to create an environment which is conducive to developing an active partnership by providing a framework for building trust and promoting healthy interaction between the public sector and private health sector. This policy, in this manner, acts as a platform for exchanging the experience and organizing resources and commitment of all partners to the increasing health needs of the people of Sudan and realizing the Millennium Development Goals".

In this Policy, the private sector was called upon to put into place Government quality standards in health care services. These included standards for grading and accrediting health facilities, performance measures, etc, to ensure that even the private sector applied the same standards as those being placed on the public health sector. There is indeed a wealth of information on the role of the private sector in public health, with evidence from across the world, presenting experiences from diverse private sector players, and services (Geaneotes, 2013, and Bishai, and Sachathep, 2015). Nonetheless, there have been challenges in implementation of these policies in both the public and private health sectors, as reported by Awadalla (2015), with some of the challenges being poor communication of implementation framework from the centre to the states and to the health facilities.

11. Patient's Right to Health and quality care

The Right to Health (UN) and access to medicines as a part of the Human Right to Health (Marks, 2009), are now accepted as the framework of health services in most countries. Patient rights associations have become a reality in quite a few countries and have taken up by professional associations, too. Studies appear to suggest that the reason why these associations have become common phenomenon, is the need to respond to a state of affairs that generally pits patients against the physician, when patients perceive that they were not receiving the expected best care from the health services; also, the physicians were considering that patients had expectations that could not be fulfilled whether these services are provided from public or private healthcare institutions.

The right to access to medicines and the right to health and quality healthcare services, are often not generally referred to in policy and strategy formulations. However, quality patient care must be provided to a patient, even if that patient is not paying. The Right to Care, the Right to Medicines and other medical products imply that the patient has the right to quality care, and that services and goods are based on quality, underpinned by ethical standards.

There are realities to face: For example, limited financial, human and material resources are evident in any country one can consider; poor policies for procurement and supply chain set-up, management, services are other areas. The inability or unwillingness to use other sector expertise in service provision (e.g. investing in the private sector to provide solutions, particularly as there is evidence of successful use of private sector in many support areas in the public health system). Given that making medicines available at every service delivery point throughout the year is a policy commitment but an operational challenge for most governments, this fact in itself possibly acts as (stated or unstated) justification for not basing planning, policies and strategies for sustainable access to medicines, on these Rights. It is correct, however, that these Rights are articulated as the foundation for access to quality health, healthcare services and medicines. That must be the starting point for formulating any health policy, strategies and operations. When used as a starting point, it will enable governments and their partners in healthcare to commit to investing in ensuring that each citizen's right to health, healthcare services and medicines are protected and are a reality.

Increasingly, in developed countries, patient- centred care is being promoted or strengthened. In these settings, it would appear that the environment, economy, resources, etc, allow for patient-centred care to be practiced, whereas in economies and environments prevailing in developing countries, with the chronic demand and high pressure on the already poorly resourced health services, attempt to offer patient-centred care might be considered a luxury that the health care staff cannot offer. Nevertheless, patient-centred care must be the basis of healthcare services and while it may not be offered in the same manner as in more developed setting (or at fee-paying service), the principle can be applied within limits.

Bouchet, et al, (2002) reported on the outcome of the implementation of the Zambia Quality Programme in Zambia's public health sector (1993-1997). The authors concluded that in spite of a 5-year programme implementing this programme that saw the establishment of Quality Assurance coaches and trainers, challenges remained in the realization of this initiative that was fundamental to the health sector reforms being undertaken at the time.

A counter-argument to this proposition of inability to provide quality care, is that most developing countries are in fact in a position to afford the minimum requirements for quality of care. The constant suggestion that a country cannot afford the basic, decent quality care service is simply a presentation of the inability to see that the people of a country have moved on, they know and are expecting their rights to be secured and met, particularly in health care. Consistently, however, the fact of affordability is hidden from the public, by virtue of the fact that leadership focuses on promoting their own inability to see that in fact the health sector has capability to provide world- class quality care to its patients across the health sector service infrastructure. Stanford Health Care best describes the experience in quality of goods and services, stating that:

"Patients and families know quality care when they experience it. A nurse's response time, a doctor's bedside manner, the hospital's atmosphere—all of these things affect how people feel about the quality of their healthcare... At Stanford Health Care, we strive to ensure that the care we provide is:

i. Safe: Avoiding injuries to patients from the care that is intended to help them.
ii. Effective: Providing services based on scientific knowledge and best practice.
iii. Patient-centred: Providing care that is respectful of and responsive to individual patient preferences, needs and values, ensuring that patients' values guide all clinical decisions.
iv. Timely: Reducing waits and sometimes harmful delays for both those who receive and provide care.
v. Efficient: Avoiding waste, including waste of equipment, supplies, ideas and energy.
vi. Equitable: Providing care that does not vary in quality because of personal characteristics such as gender, ethnicity, geographic location, and socio-economic status.
vii. Measuring quality data allows us to see where we are providing the best care and helps us identify areas for improvement."

These are fundamental expectations from the majority of patients, as stated above, in whichever community where public health services are used. Therefore, for a service provider, these elements of quality need to be built into the institutions, to be revealed whenever patients or members of the public interact with the health facility. In the Sudan National Policy on Private 'for profit' Health Sector, the FMOH calls on the private sector to attend to the patient first, and to so in a manner that preserves the rights of the patient, moving attention away from the profit goals at the time of attending the patient.

Therefore, from the perspective of healthcare, many governments have committed to provision of the quality healthcare services to their citizens. Over the years, investment has been made in building capacity to within the civil service running the health sector, to bring it up to the level where quality in goods and services have been arrived at. In so many ways, governments have realized the provision of quality medicines and other health products, through setting up stringent regulatory framework that underpin the procurement and supply of medicines. In addition, there is greater collaboration between countries in the area of pharmaceutical regulation, and the fight against the presence of counterfeit medicines in these countries. Further, some countries have recognized the challenge in access to quality medicines, by promoting the existence of regulated pharmaceutical 'health shops' as promoted by Management Sciences for Health (in Zambia, you can set up a health shop to supply human or animal health products), on the basis that retail pharmacy outlets are not being set up at a rate that a country requires.

12. Implementing a learning and practice partnership with hospitality industry

As indicated above, the health sector is also in the service industry, albeit in provision of health service. As defined above, being hospitable to a patient or other people attending the health facility is no different to how a hotel would be hospital to any visitor to that establishment. The principle of caring for that visitor applies to both sectors, and indeed, more so to the health sector. There are basic trigger questions that might start such consideration for change in the attitude towards health sector services to the patient. For example:

   i.   What does the public think if the health facility working environment or surroundings, cleanliness?
   ii. What does the public think of the health facility services?

iii. What does the public think of the quality / style of the hospital management?

iv. What does the general public think of the state of the health facility infrastructure, the surroundings and its cleanliness

v. What does the public think of the attitude of staff towards them and the patient?

vi. How are patients received at the health facility front desk or reception?

These are pertinent questions to ask if health services are going to improve and particularly if patients and the general public are to be expected to support the services.

The public health sector can indeed learn about customer service skills from the hospitality industry. It can do that by setting up learning partnership with the hospitality industry where it can undertake practical lessons in creating customer-focused services. The service training programmes that some hotels offer to the staff can also be considered for the healthcare staff, given the principles will be same. The study of the hotel will show just how the facility commits to ensuring that the client has the best of services it offers and products such as food, ensuring that that client has a memorable time, and can keep coming back to that establishment.

As already stated, Crisp et al (2000) have described partnership as one of the approaches to use in implementing a capacity building strategy, with partnership being described as revolving around individual learning, including consultation between the parties. This suggests that the health facility can enter into a learning partnership with a hotel or similar hospitality industry player, where health sector staff can have practical lessons in operating and managing a service institution, with a view to apply the principles or lesson at the health facility.

13. Linking up with the hospitality industry

In linking up with the hospitality industry, there are many areas of service that the health sector would be interested in, as indicated below:

i. How quality assurance is built into the hotel policies and strategies

ii. How quality standards are built into goods and services provided

iii. How quality standards are built and applied in the pre- qualification of suppliers of goods

iv. How quality informs the procurement and supply chain strategies for goods,

v.   How quality informs the storage of goods at premises
vi.   How Human resource management imbeds quality in Job Descriptions; tasks, accountability; operational systems; SOPs; supervision, monitoring, reporting processes
vii.   How the industry creates effective communication with clients, visitors
viii.   What structures are in place for effective corrective measures
ix.   How the industry trains its staff in quality and application of quality in services
x.   How the industry sets up an effective customer care infrastructure that address the client from the moment the clients enters the premises
xi.   How the industry uses electronic technology systems (for example, the enterprise resource planning system or ERP) to secure data capture, information development, analysis for integrated management decisions
xii.   How the industry develops and uses its internal communication systems for effective client services
xiii.   How the industry assures quality in food and beverage management throughout the year.

In most hospitality industry, every area of an establishment is considered a selling point and an opportunity to attract clients to the hotel or restaurant, by ensuring that there is no neglected area that might reflect badly on the establishment. For the health sector, the above areas of interest can be applied when engaging with, say, a hotel. As this is an opportunity to take a holistic approach to understanding why a hotel succeeds as it does, the health team can plan to learn lessons from all areas of the hotel facility.

13.1. General upkeep of premises

The hospitality industry invests in ensuring that the premises are what makes the first positive impression in the mind of the visitor; it is the strongest selling point for the business (Figure 1). The general premises and gardens will be fashioned in such a way as to invite the potential client to step across into the establishment, where those impressions formed are promised to be met. In case there is doubt that this requirement for a clean, hygienic environment is not possible in the health sector, note that the education, regulatory and professional bodies are specifically concerned about first appearances, as this reflects on the quality of service, confidence-building and trust in the service to be provided (Australia, 2012). Governments (for example, Singapore, 2013) have invested in ensuring that high standards of health facility cleanliness is the objective. Interestingly, the Government of Singapore has referenced the objective of cleanliness in health facilities to be equal to that of hotels. The Indian newspaper, the Pioneer (2014), reported how outpatients visiting a certain hospital were surprised about its clean environment, following a massive cleaning campaign the day before. The article further reports ".. only 485 patients registered themselves for various OPDs of the hospital.

Figure 1: The premises: Part of the gardens at Inzonsi Hotel on Lake Kivu, Gisenyi, Rwanda

More than 2500 patients usually visit the OPDs of the hospital in a normal day. The situation was similar in the neighbouring Doon Women hospital where less than 100 patients registered themselves for OPDs in comparison with usual OPD of 350-400 patients on a normal day. Geeta Rawat of Mokhumpur said that she was surprised to see that there is no queue of patients. The doctors too seemed happy and could be seen giving extra time to the patients". Another report, The Hans India (2018) shows the health sector staff involved in cleaning of the health facility premises. The challenge is that this sort of 'day event' happens to take place only on that day of communal effort, and is not a continuous service at the hospitals. And the question to be answered is 'Why should perimeter cleanliness be a once a month event, and not a daily service?'

13.2. **The Main Entrance:**

The main entrance of any premises in the hospitality industry, is the make or break point of interest to the visitor. The state of the main entrance will say whether a potential client will be welcomed, will find quality service, or they should turn and walk or drive away. And this does happen in this industry, that potential clients decide with their eyes. In the public health sector, health facility surroundings are sometimes not inviting, not assuring one's wellbeing, but in the absence of choice and finance to make that choice, people end up accepting to use the facility, even if their hearts tell them not to.

13.3. The Front desk and Reception

The Front Desk (or Reception) is another critical point of an establishment in the hospitality industry. Many people who have visited such businesses will attest to how negative an experience it is, when the state of the Front Desk is not welcoming. The Front Desk can be as simple or as complex as the establishment wishes (Figure 2); however, all it needs to be is a welcoming, helpful point of contact with the patient. Where advice, direction can be provided and where appointments can be made. For others, the friendly welcome cements the good decision to visit that facility, and will make the visitor a sales person for that facility. It is clear that in respect to the public health facilities across many developing countries, it is almost impossible to picture a scenario where a hospital can have the environment when there is calm, and time for healthcare workers to organise their day; where the patient and their accompanying friends or family, can find some solace as they are attended to. An organised and welcoming Front Desk is clearly a great assistance to patient management and care by clinicians, and therefore this station is a critical starting point for successful patient services, is in the interest of patient and the staff.

Figure 2: Reception: A simple, welcoming Front Desk. Sudan Red Sea Resort, Port Sudan, Sudan

13.4. The dining area

In an establishment where some customer satisfaction standards are kept and presented, eating places such as restaurants will be proud of their menu, which becomes a selling point for the establishment. This pride does not need to be based on the complexity of the dish, but many travellers and visitors can point to different types of restaurants that provide quality simple or complex meals. It is true that in some establishments, the staff waiting on tables may be the ones whose service can make a difference: there are cases where waiters have no idea of the day's menu, which can be a strange experience. Hospitality service managers will often meet with their staff before the services commences, when they can brief their staff on the day's programme as this service allows the staff to get to know what is available in terms of goods on offer to visitors (Figure 3). Not all health facilities will have catering facilities, as they will function as outpatient facilities only. However, where catering facilities are available, meals are the backbone of treatment programmes, and the health sector should consistently and sustainably invest in this service, just as it invests in the Nutrition Programme.

Figure 3: Restaurant kitchen visible to the clientele, to show quality and expertise in preparing meals. Only the confident facilities can pull this together. Rosso Trattoria Restaurant, Intercontinental Hotel, Lusaka, Zambia

13.5. The Rooms

For businesses where visitors can stay, the rooms are another selling point. From the design, to colour selection, to facilities available in the room; all these are part of the draw to the visitor. The design of rooms, in whatever class a hotel or lodge might be, is one of the important attractions for hotels/lodges. For most visitors, simple comforts of a hotel bed will be the selling point: type of mattresses, towels, what is available in room service (Figure 4). All these factors ensure one is able to enjoy their stay and sleep in that establishment. Upkeep of the rooms is also important, as there is nothing more off-putting than rooms that are damp, smell, etc.

In the hospital setting, and as seen with the examples from India given above, consistently well organised and well managed wards, and other areas where patients will rest, or spend nights, is important. The ward managers have to ensure that the wards are clean, privacy can be assured when that is required, and other events can be managed. The value of controlled visits to inpatients also provides situation when wards and other areas can be controlled and, for example, put back to normal before visiting hours.

Figure 4: Simple, clean room. Sudan Red Sea Resort, Port Sudan, Sudan

13.6. Customer services- Communicating with customers

Most hospitality establishments pride themselves in having firm customer service strategies through which all their staff pass through on a daily basis, as part of preparing for the day. In the 21st Century, we are in a period where there is massive communication initiatives and tools, as a great number of people are practically connected one to another via any type of communication tool (for example, mobile phones, internet-based communication systems). Yet, even in this period of great communication ability, institutions are still struggling to create impactful communication that helps the client or the patient. In the hospitality industry, engaging with the client is a critical service that assures success. If staff members appear not to know anything about the hotel, the menu, etc, most clients get concerned about the quality of the establishment. Having a well informed and prepared staff that communicates with the client is a critical success factor. A moment to prepare staff for the day or event is, therefore, important.

A hospital is often not seen as a customer service provider to its customer, the patient; but the healthcare giver is also a customer care service provider (see Zendesk). Of course, it is not expected that the hospital should turn out services as if it is a hotel: the issue at hand is to ensure that the patient receives services and information with the same understanding as one would expect to receive when booking into a hotel. That is, the process for a patient attending at a hospital will often be complex, difficult to understand, and often the visitor is the patient, or is acting on the behalf of another person and information is important. Such situations require careful handling with empathy (Schreiner, 2017). When patients feel that they are being taken off, they are very likely to cooperate and be receptive to services and treatment that they are provided. However, as Torpie (2014) argues, it is important not to put customer care before patient care. Indeed, in some economies, matters have developed to the level where health facilities, albeit private health facilities, are judged on the best providers of customer services (Haefner and Bean, 2017).

Figure 5: Preparing staff for service: Communication with clients starts with a well- informed, prepared staff so that they can engage with clients with confidence. Southern Sun Ridgeway Hotel, Lusaka, Zambia

In most public health facility settings, it is quite difficult for healthcare staff to have the wherewithal to handle crowds of patients and relatives, when it feels that there is crush of patients around the staff. In such a situation, which appears to be uncontrollable, healthcare staff require support from management by instilling controls in accessing services. This includes having in place better referral services, which also depend on functional primary care centres as first points of contact by the patient.

Hospitality establishments are equally adept at having smart communication strategies that inform their guests, customers about the facility, and what products and services are available to the customer; about the location and events to see during the visit by clients. Without placing any demands on the clients, the establishments recognize that communication on what is available at the premises and in the location, is a service to the client, and a means to grow their business.

13.7. Procurement and logistics

Establishments such as hotels and restaurants will pride themselves in being able to provide fresh food on a daily basis, as their core service to clients.

Procurement of products for use at the hotel may be through long-term framework agreements that may be effective for the week, month, etc. However, whichever modality, the fact is that the establishment must not run out of food, beverages, room supplies, etc. It is interesting to note that at some establishments, they can run out of supplies such as food. In such cases, it may be a strategy that once the day's allocation has been consumed, there will be no more until next day. This applies to some sensitive products, where daily procurement will have to be done. In some cases, delivery is done to the establishment, from source, to ensure that the product is as fresh as required. This requires an efficient link between procurement and logistics/delivery so that foodstuff is not left waiting to be processed. However, there are times when establishments will be out of basic products, and one wonders why there should be such an occurrence. Such situations risk the reputation of the establishment. This says something about the stock management system that is applied.

Public health facilities often have small procurement and logistics departments, and this is by design, given that much of what a health facility will need, is centrally procured, for example. However, the services by procurement and logistics must be intrinsically linked to the dynamics in the clinical and other services. Where a facility carries out its own procurement of medicines and other health products, one must ensure that all goods are procured in time to prevent out of stock situations.

13.8. Outsourcing of certain services- using the best in the service

Over time, the service industry has recognized that outsourcing of certain services is in fact a good business idea, that can save companies a lot of money, but can also result in enhancing the business. The adage is to ensure that for services that one is not good at, experts are contracted to provide those services, within the terms and conditions agreed. In public health, there are services that can be outsourced and others that cannot be outsourced. There are indeed specialized health services that can be outsourced to other external specialized health service providers. So the areas of work or services that can be outsourced to non-health service providers are not unlimited. It is in these areas that the health facility can consider outsourcing, to ensure that quality services are provided throughout the year.

The public health sector is one growth area in terms of jobs creation, particularly as the health sector tends to want to carry out all services, rather than outsource. This is again a reflection of the state of the public sector policies and governance ethos. While job creation is the outcome of decisions to 'do it ourselves', the fact of the matter is that for most areas of non-clinical work, the public health sector may not be the best performer. Further, there is always concern that the private sector will cost more, and so there is also a view that by 'doing it ourselves', the health sector is saving money. In fact, experience on the ground shows that that line of thinking results in poor services that cost the sector a lot of money.

There is difference of opinion on outsourcing hospital cleaning services. Concerns have been raised following observation of high incidence of cross infection at facilities where outsourced services are used. As discussed by many authors, this is a hotly debated matter, where on one hand there are cost-cutting measures to be addressed, through use of professional cleaning companies, and on the other, are health concerns that arise when such service providers appear to be enabling or aiding hospital acquired infections (Toffolutti, 2017 and Al-Niaimi). However, health service managers can decide over several options, but it would appear that outsourcing the cleaning of the external structures of the hospital, the tending to the gardens, walkways, etc, would be possible to outsource without too much worry about hospital acquired infections. For example, maintenance and repair of infrastructure, including routine exterior painting of buildings, repair of fixtures, repair and maintenance of walkways, etc, all appear tasks that can be contracted out to expert service providers. Services such as ambulance services can be outsourced to an expert service provider fully invested in servicing the health sector (Jaffe, 2013 and The Guardian 2017). By listing services that can be done by an external service provider, the health facility can initiate effective outsourcing of certain services, allowing the health institution to focus on its core services, but with the time and ease to manage and monitor the outsources services.

In the above very simplified illustration of the situation found at hospitality industry, I have attempted to show that it is possible to use this sector as a learning ground for practices that can inform the health sector. In planning learning engagements with the hotels or other such players, the health team should prepare to learn from all aspects of the hotel to see how all these facets of services link together to result in service that results in the rating that hotel maintains. In line with a comment by Torpie et al (2014) referred to above, the purpose of this engagement with hospitality is to learn about the similarities in the objective of care and service to the client. It is also to learn how the services provided by the hospitality industry, the strategies used, can be adapted or applied in the public health sector for better engagement with and responses from the patient. The aim must be about ensuring that there is quality healthcare services to the patient, and so lessons on building and applying quality services is the justification for engaging with other services providers that exist on quality assurance- based provision of goods and services.

14. **Using Job Descriptions as an instrument to imbed quality assurance in jobs**

I have suggested that the public health sector can be transformed into an enterprise that provides quality health care services to the public. It can do so by learning from the best in the service industry, mainly the hospitality industry, although other services, for example the airline industry, can also provide quality, valuable lessons. Simple working partnerships and practical training programmes can all go towards changing the way services are provided. If this strategy can be considered, then one way to secure the change is to ensure that the performers of those jobs are enabled, guided to ensure that they only practice in one way: the quality way.

There are thousands of books on quality management, and these are available for the reader to read and apply to their situation. One way of implementing change, is to ensure that the basis of the job performance is as clear to the management as it is to the performer of those duties. The challenge in the business of Human Resource management has often been that we expect the staff member to know exactly how to interpret the job requirement notes, into a practice that meets what we think we want to see out of that job. However, this ability to translate/interpret guidelines is also subjective. The outcome expected requires that both the supervisor and the performer have the same understanding and, therefore, practical interpretation of what the job statement is stating. Clearly this is not always going to be the case, if at all. Therefore, rather than question the intelligence of the performer, it is best to craft directives that help the performer to understand the expected outcome and the 'how to', to ensure that the outcome is achieved. One way to do that is in creating a practical job description document that explains and gives guidance to the performer in their duties.

The civil service tends to have basic job descriptions that are created to address a common service level. For example, the civil service might have a job description for say, Management Position Grade 1, which applies to that position in all ministries across the government establishment, irrespective of whether that position will be in agriculture, health, home affairs, or finance. The nuances will indicate what the specific functions will be in the respective sector (agriculture, health, etc). In some positions, such as procurement, the job descriptions and details thereof, are the same across the government establishment. The idea is to enable an officer to move from one ministry (for example, works) to another (for example, health) in the same capacity. So, a procurement officer who has been procuring goods and services for construction of bridges, might find themselves working as a procurement officer in the health sector, where they have to procure health commodities. Of course, while many health officers have been moved to higher offices in other government sectors, to policy makers, etc, it is unlikely that a nurse would be re-assigned to work as an agricultural extension officer, even if the two positions may be at the same government level of employment. But, for the majority of common services, such as accountant, receptionists, procurement, planning, etc, these positions ten to carry generic job descriptions, which means that the holders of these position can move from one government sector to another.

14.1. Designing a quality- based Job Description

Notwithstanding the main job description that arises from the employer, it is expected that each sector and at each level of work, there will be provided the appropriate operational guidelines or Standard Operating Procedures (SOPs) that the job-holder will be required to apply. The biggest mistake that is made in public services, is to assume that simply because one is a nurse, midwife, laboratory technician, physiotherapist, dentist, doctor or pharmacist, that these professional bodies must know how to provide a patient-based service. In fact, that is the expectation one ought to have, primarily because training in patient care calls for training in quality care. Quality care, being hospitable, empathetic, are all part of the backbone of healthcare in whichever health service one is. Reisenwitz (2017) provides advice on steps to take by a physician when running a private health service. These principles, such as acknowledging the patient, introducing oneself to the patient, and explaining what the process shall be in their care, all add to making an effective patient-centred services. However, along the way, we appear to have lost the plot in creating a patient-centred service.

The design of the additional guidance document provides an opportunity to define areas of responsibility, the day-to-day tasks that must be performed in key areas of work, and statement on accountability held by the incumbent in respect to that duty/role. For each area of work, for example stores and stock management, dispensing services, capacity development services to staff, monitoring of staff performance, etc, stating the areas of responsibility, the tasks to be undertaken and areas of accountability, should help the incumbent to better perform in their duties. Description of areas of work for which the office of the Hospital Pharmacist is solely accountable for. For example, the work of the hospital pharmacist is to ensure that the application of pharmaceutical policies and strategies is taking place. Further, that pharmacy staff are carrying out the services in the manner described in each job description, and that there are resources available to ensure provision of quality services to the patient and the staff at the hospital. In that task, and particularly in the public sector, the hospital pharmacist has an elaborate hierarchy of support at the health facility, district, province and from headquarters. Drafting a document that provides guidance on the duties to be carried out is also an enhancement to the SOPs that now go into greater detail on the steps to be carried out in teach task.

14.2. Responsibilities, Tasks and Accountability

Staff members are responsible for several activities, and each activity contains specific tasks that must be carried out to produce an outcome. Officers can delegate certain responsibilities and tasks. However, officers cannot delegate the accountability they have for the responsible areas that they hold. It is the position holder that is accountable for the success or failure of the duties that are described in the job description. For this reason, each staff member needs to have a clear list of areas of responsibility, the tasks that they are expected to perform on a daily basis and what they are accountable for within that sphere of work. For example, the hospital pharmacist is accountable for the implementation of a wide range of pharmaceutical services at the hospital. In most developing countries, the hospital pharmacist is also a part of a broad pharmaceutical management virtual office that might include the district and provincial pharmaceutical team. In public health, the extent of the team will include stakeholders from non-government organisations, and also the private healthcare organisations. The areas of responsibility will encompass the following:

   i.   Pharmaceutical Services to the patient
   ii. Pharmaceutical services to the healthcare team at hospital
   iii. Information on medicines management

iv. Quality Control and Quality Assurance
v. Forecasting, quantification, budgeting, and procurement or ordering of medicines
vi. Pharmacy staff capacity building, staff management
vii. General communication on pharmaceutical services, products availability, etc
viii.   Project implementation & management
ix. Monitoring, evaluation, reporting on pharmaceutical services at the hospital

For example, with regard to Quality Control and Quality Assurance, the pharmacist would be responsible for ensuring that the hospital is applying the correct measures for the storage and management of medicines at the hospital, and is adhering to the regulations in that respect. The task of the pharmacist will be to do that on a daily basis, all medicines are kept at the correct storage conditions in the pharmacy or any other approved location of medicines such as hospital inpatient wards. The pharmacist is, therefore, accountable for ensuring that all medicines are at the correct storage condition at all times. In that way, the SOPs will provide the details on how correct storage of medicines must be applied at a health facility. Implementation of the SOPs will be a necessary step for the pharmaceutical staff, based on the fact that they take personal liability if there is failure to do so. Annex 1 is an example of a simple matrix of responsibilities, tasks and accountability areas.

15. Performance-based remuneration in public health services

Reich, et al (2016), reported that for a long time health system strengthening, more than just enabling healthcare services and supplies to be available, became the focus of attention for development aid to public health services in the developing countries; because there was a need to create resilient public health institutions that would sustainably manage, finance the health sector, and provide quality healthcare services. In development programme financing, donor and recipient countries have applied the results-based financing (RBF) or performance-based financing (PBF), or payment for performance (P4P), which aims to pay institutions or individual health workers for achieving agreed upon results.

Results-based financing (RBF) as a method of financing health programmes, including the provision of services. Grittner (2013) reports on several results-based initiatives, and has defined RBF as "any programme where the principal sets financial or other incentives for an agent to deliver predefined outputs or outcomes and rewards the achievement of these results upon verification", earlier defined by Musgrove (2010). Further, Grittner expands on this, stating that "… RBF in development cooperation, the principal is usually a national or sub-national government body of a developing country. The agent is an implementing agency (in the case of performance-based financing) or an individual (in the case of a conditional cash transfer – CCT). If RBF targets the supply side, it is also called performance-based financing and aims at setting incentives for service providers to deliver good performance. Indicators are set by the principal – often together with the agent. Payment takes place against achievement of these predefined indicators". According to Africa Health Forum (2013), "Results-Based Financing (RBF) is an instrument that links financing to pre-determined results, with payment made only upon verification that the agreed-upon results have actually been delivered. The RBF strategy can help improve both supply- and demand- sided performance of health systems striving for Universal Health Coverage. In an RBF programme, payments are made based on the quantity and quality of health services delivered after verification".

The expectation is that as financial resources are made available to institutions or individuals, their performance will improve, and over time, that culture of positive performance for positive results, will be institutionalized, to the extent that this way of working becomes second nature to staff and the institution as a whole. However, when Grittner (2013) studied monetary incentives for good performance, she noticed that "PBF tends to focus on outputs rather than on health outcomes, and on quantity rather than on quality", and concluded that "There is no sufficient evidence that monetary incentives trigger better performance of healthcare providers. On the one hand, observation and surveys suggest that non-monetary incentives, such as more empowerment and involvement of staff, more flexibility, or fear of reputation loss, may have played an important role concerning improvements in healthcare delivery. On the other hand, there are strong reasons to believe that PBF schemes will also set perverse incentives and have undesired effects, since there is evidence from other results-based approaches as well as from PBF in other settings for the existence of perverse incentives".

Experiences reported by Grittner suggest that to apply and evaluate any RBF scheme is fraught with too many factors that would require assessing in order to get the best picture of the impact of the financing arrangement. However, it is clear that financing of an institution that is providing a service, can be based on agreed performance and milestones, that can be as complex or as simple as the parties agree to apply. In another report, the WB showed that PBF had achieved the expected impact, and should be considered for extension to other programme and services areas (Chansa, 2015). This strategy appears to be possible to apply when the whole institution is being assessed in terms of meeting agreed performance objectives. Therefore, one could apply this strategy to a situation where quality service provision by a health facility, set against common specific milestones, can be rewarded in form of additional financing to that institution. However, in some other setting, staff rewards have been applied, based on a staff performance appraisal.

Most institutions undertake some form of staff performance appraisal, and this should not be uncommon to the public health sector. Nuti, et al (2013) report on the success of a performance appraisal system that had shown success, based on the observation of five elements of success, which were the visual reporting system, the linkage between the performance evaluation system and Chief Executive Officer's reward system, the public disclosure of data, the high level of employees' and managers' involvement into the entire process and the strong political commitment. Performance management and appraisal has challenges, as reported by Mahapa, et al (2015) the lack of real investment in the process by the stakeholders resulted in a poorly implemented process that was not able to provide benefits from the tool. Whether this approach can be applied in the civil service in developing countries, is a matter to be considered.

16. **Engagement of the private sector in provision of services**

The Zambia National Health Strategic Plan (2011- 2015), committed the country to the involvement of the private sector in provision of specialized healthcare services, among other services, and would use the private sector using such strategies as public private partnerships (Zambia National Health Strategic Plan, 2011-2015). Indeed, in health care financing, the Strategy called for "Institutionalise high cost wings in hospitals and explore co-opting private sector to run private wings (PPPs) as well as specialised services more generally" (page 91). In his comment on Zambia Vision 2030, Bikalemesa, J. M. (2014), suggests that Zambia aspire to a country which by 2030 will have a:

i. Diversified and balanced and strong industrial sector, a modern agricultural sector and an efficient and productive services sector; and be a

ii. Regional centre of excellence in health and education;

Together with the direction taken by the Government in the NHSP (2011- 2015), one sees that there is an opportunity for directly involving the private sector in not in the production of goods, but also in the provision of services. Thus, where the public health sector has no immediate skills, expertise and capability to provide certain services with the required quality, it should be possible to exercise the facilities provided for under national policies and strategies, when the private sector with appropriate capability, can be applied to the task at hand. These tasks may include the management of institutions, the manufacture of goods and the provision of services.

17. Why is Quality in Public Health Services important?

As indicated above, the purpose of engaging with the hospitality industry is to learn the basis for application of quality in their service and goods provided to the clients, and that from that common starting point, how that approach in the hospitality industry can be applied in the public health sector of developing countries. The level of support to human resource capacity building in the public health sector demand that there are different strategies applied to creating solutions to achieve quality service provision to the patient. Learning directly from sectors that work with similar challenges, but succeed, is probably one simple innovation that can be applied incapacity building and systems strengthening strategies, and in this case, engagement with best performing players in the hospitality industry seems to be an effective and affordable option that can be sustained over the long-term period.

The hospitality industry survives on providing quality assured goods and services. The hospitality industry invests in putting in place operational systems that will enable them reach their customer service targets in the shortest possible time, and to do so sustainably, achieving profitable results within stated timeframes. Further, well-performing hotels ensure that they provide quality service to a visitor or client, so that the client can come back again and again. It is possible that the impact of that positive experience will compel the visitor to spread the news to others, about how good the hotel is. Having this practical lesson in creating a customer-focused service to positive results, is the strategy that the health sector can learn. These positive, customer-focused practices, are the key lessons that the health sector can learn from the hotel industry and apply at the health facility, resulting in patient-focused services. The benefit of learning from the hospitality industry would be less of a burden to the health facility, and more meaningful than running high cost workshops only (most likely to be held in the same hotels).

17.1. Recommendations:

Quality-based, patient-focused public health services will have a positive impact on the patient, the health sector, and the health of the country as a whole. With quality assured services in place, where accountability, transparency and effective application of management and services, public confidence in the health sector will be positive and remain that way. Further, for an effective health sector, better and joined-up operational systems and tools must be applied that provide for evidence-based decision-making, and more effective support to staff. How to create and sustain a customer or patient-focused quality service is the challenge that has dogged the public health sector, to date, in spite of steep and necessary investment in capacity building programmes.

However, one such solution is to consider learning from the hospitality industry, with which the health sector has a lot in common. There are some practical steps that institutions in the health sector can take to engage and work with the hospitality industry. In the first instance, it would appear that learning from sectors that apply quality standards in their services and goods, would be the most practical way to learn for implementation. In doing so, there are fundamentals to be put in place by the health sector:

i. Ensure that you have written institutional quality assurance policy, which, if it exists, responds to the national quality assurance policy for provision of quality goods and services (UNIDO, 2016; COMESA, 2009; Sudan FMOH, 2018)
ii. Define or get assistance in defining quality parameters that must apply in any area of work at the health facility or institution
iii. Identify your quality service needs as part of skills development for staff
iv. Recognize the fact that players within the hospitality industry are not the same; this is important in identifying and entering into a learning partnership with the hospitality industry player
v. Obtain strategy to use for engaging the hospitality industry entity that you shall work with: Will you be required to procure the training services of the hotel, or not?
vi. Identify the best in the hospitality industry in your location from whom you are seeking lessons to learn

vii. Management to meet and discuss quality training requirements with the hospitality industry entity

viii. Undertake initial study on how the hotel facility selected provides its services; prepare a report as part of the justification

ix. Create a justification for whatever strategy will formally be used to engage the hospitality entity, bearing in mind that a 5 star hotel is quite different from a facility with no star

x. Work out the cost for application of a hands-on training programme that applies, for example, half a day for one week

xi. Identify the areas of your institution that you shall start the training programme with; this could be a mixture staff across the institution, or targeted to specific areas of the institution (e.g., catering; procurement; environment management; infrastructure, etc)

xii. Draft a Scope of Learning that you want to receive from the hospitality industry entity, and subject that to the hospitality industry entity for them to prepare a programme

xiii. Agree on how to adapt or enhance your SOPs to ensure that the new way of working links in with your institutional Quality Assurance Policy

xiv. Agree on how to apply the lessons learned and also how to measure successful implementation of lessons learned

xv. Make a long-term agreement on provision of this service, whose application must be made in such a way that the training programme is possible, and benefits both parties

xvi. Set a start date

Learning from the hospitality industry must result in practical decisions at the health facility, and that is why this resource is more a practical option than an academic, theoretical learning process. The institutions have to put into place a strategy change the way staff learn about service provision with the patient care continuum, so that quality of care is in built into each step, and services are assessed with quality parameters structured into the processes. That way, standard operating procedures become based on provision of caring, quality services at all times, and the management of staff, services and the patient become founded on quality. This will require deliberate enhancements to Job Descriptions, to ensure that the roles, tasks, responsibilities and areas of accountability for each staff are stated clearly and staff are fully aware of the milestones.

The institution can then more easily apply organisational reforming strategies such as applying the Balanced Score Card (Balanced Scorecard Institute, and Bernard Marr and Company) approach, and expect to gain benefits thereof, much more easily, as the staff are already knowledgeable about the importance of quality performance for quality service delivery.

18. Conclusion:

Performance of the public health sector facilities and related institutions is a subject of much debate, given that there is much expected from these institutions by their government and citizens. The quality of services provided to the patient has a direct effect on how the community perceives the health institution. There are issues of trust, reliability, and confidence in the facility and services provided from it. As discussed here, the patient's perception of quality is much simpler than we might imagine. A well-managed and administered health facility, whose services can immediately be judged as trustworthy, reliable and of high quality, has a far reaching and positive impact on the general public. Learning from sectors or institutions that provide demonstrable and sustained quality services will enable the public sector to translate public health commitments and goals into a reality. This approach should not be dismissed as bringing on board 'commercial business practices', a subject which quite often results in defensive response from the public sector. Rather, the public health sector will be learning skills on applying its policies and strategies with the efficiency and effectiveness that underlies the health establishment, which is a part of the service industry. Public health facilities, that are demonstrably well-run and have quality-focused staff who are patient-focused, will be facilities that achieve their institutional targets. In so doing, the facility will impart confidence in the users of those facilities.

This simple strategy of learning for the hospitality industry may be the most effective way to meeting the Sustainable Development Goals for Health. To be realized aspirations require leadership, sustained investment in developing of demonstrably functioning policies and strategies, partnerships and indeed human and financial resources. Over the last 60 years, many developing countries have changed their economic, education and services situations to the extent that there is recognition of the right to quality goods and services provided through the health sector. At no time in the evolution of countries in the developing world has there been so much awareness about rights: to information, ideas, to quality products and services. People are travelling the world and learning, and comparing goods, services, leadership and management styles, and have gained better understanding of what they should expect as citizens, of what can and cannot work. In this day and age, it is quite patronizing to the intelligence of the so-called 'common' man to suggest that 'they must be thankful of what we are doing for them'.

Equally, from a commercial perspective, there is recognition that developing countries should focus on creating quality in goods and services, if they are to be competitive, if they are to develop, and if they are to retain their experts. It goes without saying that to achieve this end-point requires policy and strategic changes in the way countries are governed, how resources are applied, and how both public and private sectors apply themselves to such an objective. To that end, institutions such as COMESA and UNIDO have promoted, supported and assisted countries to formulate their quality assurance policies for manufacture and provision of goods and services with a view to encourage the provision of quality goods and services to their citizens and to promote trade and commerce. The role of partnership in national development initiatives is one of the most important realizations coming out of the creation of institutions such as the UN. These institutions that have become part and parcel of nationhood for many countries over the last 70 years, provide support to the process of national growth and transformation.

However, these institutions are not designed to be 'ATMs' for funds or technical assistance. They have a purpose that, where services have been accepted and applied within agreements, have resulted in solutions that otherwise a country would not have had the means to achieve. Indeed, these institutions can be applied to support most challenging of demands, such as the construction of quality goods and services for the benefit of children, men and women. A common occurrence in public services is that there is ability to unlearn the efficiencies that have been gained. As presented here, while pilots may be carried out with positive results, area of work such as building quality assurance in service provision tends to fall by the wayside, as focus changes to other ongoing matters, which, if pilots are implemented, would actually serve those demanding areas well. Such situations can result in setting efforts, aspirations back many years. The phenomenon of drastic changes to policies and strategies can have a negative impact in the process of building a quality foundation in service provision, and in a way could be considered one of the greatest risks to public health services. For many countries, the policy of a consultative, collaborative partnership-based health service has helped ensure smooth transition is undertaken, ensuring that ongoing initiatives and strategies that are building quality services, do continue. In an environment where reform process are not managed in this constructive way, the gains that have been achieved are easily swept away in favour of attending to the 'new challenge'. One would hope, however, that when public health services become founded on quality assurance in provision of goods and services, that state of affairs would result in building a process that informs and secures policy and strategy development, capacity building services, management and governance strategies in the health sector.

19. REFERENCES:

1. African Union (Organisation of African Unity): Abuja Declaration on HIV/AIDS, Tuberculosis and other Infectious Diseases', April 2001, at http://www.un.org/ga/aids/pdf/abuja_declaration.pdf
2. WHO: Abuja Declaration- Ten Years On, 2011, at

   http://www.who.int/healthsystems/publications/abuja_report_aug_2011.pdf
3. Institute for Health Metrics and Evaluation: World spends more than $200 billion to make countries healthier, at https://www.sciencedaily.com/releases/ 2015/06/150616123606.htm
4. UNDP Capacity Development Practice Note (2008). United Nations Development Programme. New York, NY 10017 USA. Accessed online at http://www.undp.org/ capacity/ourapproach.shtml.
5. Pallangyo, W and Reese, C. J.: 'Local Government Reform Programme and Human Resource Capacity Building in Africa: Evidence from Local Government Authorities (LGAs) in Tanzania', in International Journal of Public Administration, Volume 33, 2010 - Issue 12-13: Decentralisation and Local Governance in Developing and Trans i t ional Count r ies , at ht tps ://www. tandfonl ine.com/doi/abs/10.1080/01900692.2010.514714
6. Dada, J. O.: Human Capacity Building Challenges- Towards Improved Service Delivery in Africa, at http://unpan1.un.org/intradoc/groups/public/documents/aapam/unpan025978 .pdf
7. Van de Werf, H: Food and Agriculture Organisation Draft paper: Evaluating the Impact of Capacity Building Activities in the field of Food Quality and Safety, 2007
8. Prashanth, N.S., et al: Evaluation of capacity-building program of district health managers in India: a contextualized theoretical framework, in Frontiers in Public Health, Public Health Education and Promotion, 2014, at
   https://www.frontiersin.org/articles/10.3389/fpubh.2014.00089/full
9. Crisp, R.S., et al: Four approaches to capacity building in health: consequences for measurement and accountability, in Health Promotion International, Volume 15, Issue 2, 1 June 2000, Pages 99–107, https://doi.org/10.1093/heapro/15.2.99
10. Wikipedia: https://en.wikipedia.org/wiki/Hospital; and at https://en.wikipedia.org/wiki/Hospitality
11. Lonely Planet, at https://www.lonelyplanet.com; https://www.tripadvisor.com/
12. Wikipedia: Hotel Ratings, at https://en.wikipedia.org/wiki/Hotel_rating

13. Hotel Stars, at https://www.hotelstars.eu/criteria/
    and http://traveltips.usatoday.com/hotels-star-rated-21440.html
14. Tourismni: https://tourismni.com/startup-advice/quality-grading/touristaccommodation-grading/
15. AHA: Australian Hotels: Contributing to economic growth and national prosperity, at http://aha.org.au/wp-content/uploads/2013/07/AHA-National-Policy-Platform-2013.pdf
16. American Hotel & Lodging Association: The U.S. Hotel Industry: Driving Growth, Jobs & The Economy, at https://www.ahla.com/sites/default/files/Driving%20Growth%2C%20Jobs%20and%20the%20Economy.pdf
17. Morissette, C: Government revenue attributable to tourism, 2011, at https://www.destinationcanada.com/sites/default/files/archive/2011-12- 01/ Intelligence_GovernmentRevenueAttributableToTourism_2011_EN.pdf
18. World Travel and Tourism Council: Travel and Tourism Economic Impact-South Africa 2017, at https://www.wttc.org/-/media/files/reports/economic-impactresearch/countries- 2017/southafrica2017.pdf
19. Samsuddin, S.B.: Logistics and Supply Chain Management in the hotel industry: Impact on hotel performance at Naza Talyya hotel, Melaka. Report submitted to the Faculty of Technology Management and Technopreneurship (FPTT), Universiti Teknikal Malaysia Melaka in fulfilment for Bachelor of Technopreneurship with Honours, 2013
20. Nicolaides, A. and Peristeris, O.: Logistics and Customer Service in the Hospitality Industry, in African Journal of Hospitality, Tourism and Leisure, Vol 1 (3), 2011
21. Dubai Hospitals and Health Centres, at http://www.dubaicityinfo.com/Health/ dubai_hospitals.aspx;
22. Uganda Ministry of Health: Uganda Health Sector Development Plan 2015-16_2019-20, 2015.
23. WHO: Health System Profile-Sudan, in Regional Health System Observatory, 2006
24. Sternberg, S.: Hospital Groups Debate How to Grade Quality of Care, at https://health.usnews.com/health-news/hospital-of-tomorrow/articles/2016-04-08/hospital-groups-debate-how-to-grade-quality-of-care
25. Al-Damen, R: Health Care Service Quality and Its Impact on Patient Satisfaction "Case of Al-Bashir Hospital", in International Journal of Business and Management; Vol. 12, No. 9; 2017
26. Singh, R: Patients' Perception towards Government Hospitals in Haryana, in VSRDTNTJ, Vol. I (4), 2010, 198-206, at

http://citeseerx.ist.psu.edu/viewdoc/ download? doi=10.1.1.466.882&
rep=rep1&type=pdf

27. A Mining Health Initiative case study: First Quantum Mining Limited,
Zambia: Lessons in Government Engagement, January 2013, at
http://www.hanshep.org/ member-area/programmes/mining-health-
initiative/jan-2013-zambia-case-studyfirst-quantum-mining.pdf

28. International Council on Mining and Metals: Community health programs in
the mining and metals industry, 2013, at
https://www.icmm.com/website/publications/pdfs/5788.pdf

29. Zambia Ministry of Commerce, Trade and Industry: Zambia Quality Policy,
2011

30. COMESA: The COMESA Standards, Metrology, Conformity Assessment
and Accreditation Policy, 2009

31. UNIDO: Guide for the Development of National Quality Policies, 2016

32. WHO: Quality and accreditation in health care services: A Global Review,
2003

33. Botswana Ministry of Trade and Industry: National Quality Policy for
Botswana, 2015

34. Federal Ministry of Nigeria: National Quality Assurance Policy for
Pharmaceutical Products

35. WHO: WHO good manufacturing practices (GMP) for pharmaceutical
products: main principles. In WHO Technical Report Series, No. 961, 2011

36. Zambia Public Procurement Authority (ZPPA): Zambia Public Procurement
Act, 2008 and Regulations, 2011

37. Gabra, M.: Session 6- Enhancing Pharmaceutical Procurement; The Johns
Hopkins Bloomberg School of Health, John Hopkins University, in
collaboration with USAID and Management Sciences for Health, 2006

38. Global Fund to fight AIDS, TB and Malaria: Procurement and Supply
Management, 2009

39. World Health Organization: WHO good distribution practices for
pharmaceutical products, in WHO Technical Report Series, No. 957, Annex
5, 2010

40. European Union: Guidelines of 7 March 2013 on Good Distribution Practice
of Medicinal Products for Human Use

41. Muscatello, J. R. and Chen, I.J.: Enterprise Resource Planning (ERP)
Implementations: Theory and Practice, at
http://www.igi-global.com/chapter/enterprise-resource-planning-erp-
implementations/36759?camid=4v1

42. Buisson, J: Patient pack dispensing: why has such a good idea been so long
in arriving? In The Pharmaceutical Journal, Vol 270, p 683- 685, May 2003.

43. East Cheshire NHS Trust: Dispensing and Storage of Medicines Policy, 2017.
44. Ministry of Health, Malaysia: Drug Control Authority: Guide for Implementation of Patient Dispensing Pack for Pharmaceutical Products in Malaysia, 2008
45. Leung, N-H, Z., et al: The Impact of Inventory Management on Stock-Outs of Essential Drugs in Sub-Saharan Africa: Secondary Analysis of a Field Experiment in Zambia, in PLoS ONE 11(5), 2015 | DOI:10.1371/journal.pone.0156026, May 2016
46. Medical Board of Australia: Guidelines for advertising of regulated health services, 2010
47. Milton Friedman: The Social Responsibility of Business is to Increase its Profits, in The New York Times Magazine, September 13, 1970
48. Sudan Federal Ministry Of Health: National Policy for Private 'for Profit' Health Sector, 2009
49. Geaneotes, A.: The Role of the Private Sector in Expanding Health Access to the Base of the Pyramid, in International Finance Corporation / World Bank Group publication, (2 0 1 3?) a t h t t p s : / / w w w. i f c . o r g / w p s / w c m / c o n n e c t / 5be1a00043e7653faabcba869243d457/60939_IFC_HealthReport_FINAL.pdf?MOD=AJPERES
50. Bishai, D. and Sachathep, K.: The role of the private sector in health systems, in Health Policy and Planning 2015;30:i1
51. Awadalla, H.M.I.: Implementation of Quality Assurance Program in Sudanese Public Hospitals: Lessons Learned, in Journal of Medicine and Medical Research Vol. 3(2): 7-14, April, 2015
52. United Nations: The Right to Health (Fact Sheet No.31)
53. Marks, S.P.: Access to Essential Medicines as a Component of the Right to Health. In Health: A Human Rights Perspective, 2009.
54. Bouchet B. et al: The Zambia Quality Assurance Program: Successes and Challenges, in International Journal of Quality in Health Care, Vol 14, Supplement 1, p89-95; 2002
55. Stanford Health Care: Quality Care for Every Patient. At https://stanfordhealthcare.org/about-us/quality.html
56. Management Sciences for Health, Centre for Market Innovations: Accredited Drug Dispensing Outlets (ADDO), at https://healthmarketinnovations.org/program/accrediteddrug- dispensing-outlets-addo

57. Australian Government, Department of Education and Workplace Relations, Industry Skills Council: SIRCCPM503 Manage pharmacy premises and equipment, 14th June 2012

58. Ministry of Health, Singapore: Environmental Cleaning Guidelines for Healthcare Settings, June 2013

59. The Pioneer: OPD Visitors Surprised by Clean Hospital Premises, 4th October 2014, at https://www.dailypioneer.com/state-editions/dehradun/opd-visitors-surprised-by-cleanhospital- premises.html

60. The Hans India: Medical staff joins hands to clean hospital. 27 June 2018, at http:// www.thehansindia.com/posts/index/Khammam-Tab/2018-06-27/Medical-staff-joinshands- to-clean-hospital/392792

61. Zendesk: Providing Support at a Critical Time: Hospital Customer Service, at https://www.zendesk.com/support/features/hospital-customer-service/

62. Schreiner, D.: Why We Need Customer Service at a Hospital Level. In Cerner, at https:// www.cerner.com/blog/why-we-need-customer-service-at-a-hospital-level

63. Torpie, K.: Customer service vs. Patient care. In Patient Experience Journal, Vol 1, Issue 1, 2014

64. Haefner, M and Bean, M: 16 hospitals with great customer service. In Berker's Review, 2017 at https://www.beckershospitalreview.com/hospital-management-administration/ 11-hospitals-with-great-customer-service.html

65. Toffolutti, V. et al: Outsourcing cleaning services increases MRSA incidence: Evidence from 126 English acute trusts, in Social Science & Medicine (174) 2017

66. Al-Niaimi, S: Hospital cleaning: In-house versus outsourcing, at http://www.cleanmiddleeast.ae/articles/245/hospital-cleaning-in-house-versusoutsourcing.html

67. Jaffe, H.: Debating the pros and cons of outsourcing ambulance service. In Las Vegas Review Journal, 2013, at https://www.reviewjournal.com/local/local-columns/herbjaffe/debating-the-pros-and-cons-of-outsourcing-ambulance-service/

68. The Guardian (International Edition): Private ambulances increasingly used to respond to 999 calls, 2017. At https://www.theguardian.com/society/2017/feb/03/privateambulances-increasingly-used-999-calls-england-spending-nhs-crisis

69. Reisenwitz, C.: The Best Doctors Enhance Their Patient Care With These 3 Tips, at https://blog.capterra.com/best-doctors-enhance-their-patient-care-with-these-3-tips/

70. Reich, M. R. et al: Lessons from 20 Years of Capacity Building for Health Systems Thinking, in Health Systems & Reform, 2:3, 213-221, 2016

71. Grittner, A.M.: Results-based Financing- Evidence from performance-based financing in the health sector. Discussion paper of the German Development Institute, June 2013

72. Musgrove, P.: Rewards for good performance or results : a short glossary; World Bank Washington, DC, 2010

73. Africa Health Forum: Results Based Financing for Health, 2013 at http://siteresources.worldbank.org/INTAFRICA/Resources/AHF-results-basedfinancing. pdf

74. Chansa, C. et al: Linking Results to Performance: Evidence from a Results Based Financing Pre-Pilot Project in Katete District, Zambia. A World Bank report, April 2015

75. Nuti, S. et al: Assessing the effectiveness of a performance evaluation system in the public health care sector: some novel evidence from the Tuscany region experience. In Journal of Management & Governance Vol 17, Issue 1, pp 59–69, 2013

76. Mahapa, M. et al: Performance Management Hurdles in a Public Health Sector Organisation in Zimbabwe. In European Scientific Journal, Vol.11, No.32, 2015

77. Ministry of Health, Zambia: National Health Strategic Plan, 2011-2015

78. Bikalemesa, J. M.: Zambia Vision 2030, at http://fortuneofafrica.com/zambia/2014/02/08/zambia-vision-2030/

79. Sudan FMOH: (Draft) Sudan National Quality Assurance Policy for Pharmaceutical and other Health Products, 2017-2021

80. Balanced Scorecard Institute: Balanced Scorecard Basics, at http:// www.balancedscorecard.org/BSC-Basics/About-the-Balanced-Scorecard

81. Bernard Marr and Co: The 7 Key Benefits Of Using A Balanced Scorecard, at https://www.bernardmarr.com/default.asp?contentID=972

ANNEX 1: Responsibilities, Tasks and Accountabilities of the Hospital Pharmacist

Background:

The work of the hospital pharmacist is to ensure that pharmaceutical services are taking place in line with health sector pharmaceutical policies, strategies, rules and regulations. The pharmacist applies these services to ensure that healthcare services are carried out without interruption due to lack of appropriate pharmaceutical products and services.

Purpose of this document:

This document provides a detailed description of areas of work for which the Hospital Pharmacist is responsible and accountable for. The information in this document is based on the general JD for the Hospital Pharmacist, including WHO recommendations for good pharmaceutical practice, as would apply to hospital pharmacy practice.

Responsibilities, Tasks and Accountability:

In any work place, each staff member needs to have a clear understanding of the areas of responsibility, the tasks involved, and thus the areas of duty which they are accountable for within that sphere of work. The pharmacist is responsible for several activities, and each activity contains specific tasks for service outcomes; these areas of responsibility are those where the pharmacist is the accountable officer. The pharmacist has most of these functions already delegated to other members of the pharmacy who come under the supervision of the pharmacist. However, delegation does not remove the issue of being accountable and answerable for those functions, even as they are performed by other staff members, as those duties are inherent in the position held by the pharmacist.

The Hospital Pharmacist is accountable for the implementation of a wide range of pharmaceutical services at the hospital. In that regard, the Hospital Pharmacist has a specific role that he/she plays to ensure that there is consistent and uninterrupted access to diagnostic systems, treatment tools and other services. The Hospital Pharmaceutical is by design a part of a broad pharmaceutical management, supervision, monitoring, evaluation, reporting and support infrastructure and hierarchy. The team will also include pharmaceutical staff and services from other stakeholders in the public health sector, such as staff from NGO and private sector establishments.

Key areas of Responsibility and Accountability:

The following is an example of a list of duties that apply to the hospital pharmacist, and is by no means conclusive:

1. Pharmaceutical advisory and monitoring, and reporting services
2. Pharmaceutical support services to the clinical management teams
3. General medicines management services at the health facility
4. Quality Control and Quality Assurance
5. Operations monitoring, evaluation and reporting
6. Planning and budgeting
7. Training and Capacity Building
8. Leadership in pharmaceutical area at the hospital level
9. Pharmacy staff management
10. General communication on pharmaceutical services
11. Communication on the supply chain status
12. Preparing medicines and medical supply orders
13. Project implementation & management
14. Reporting on state of the pharmaceutical services at hospital

The role of the hospital pharmacist evolves with the evolutions in the health public health sector, and from time to time, the pharmacist will pick up new services. This is what has happened, as we see, with the pharmacist being responsible for management of all medical, laboratory supplies, etc, as part of health commodity stock management. In some countries, these responsibilities may be covered by health sector policy statements; in others, it is out of policy on integration of the procurement and supply chain management of medicines and medical supplies.

Matrix of Responsibility, Task and Accountability

The following is a description of strategic areas of work for the hospital pharmacist. These areas of work are described in a matrix that shows what the core responsibilities are, what are the tasks that need to be done, and what the pharmacist is accountable for in that role. This matrix is by no means conclusive.

1. Leadership, Management of the Pharmaceutical team

The Hospital Pharmacist is the lead pharmaceutical officer at the hospital level, and is the first point of reference for all the pharmaceutical issues at that health facility. The hospital pharmacist is accountable for and takes leadership in provision, supervising, advising, managing, monitoring, analysing and reporting on impact of pharmaceutical service policies, strategies, rules, legal and regulatory matters related to medicines and provision of medicines. By default, the pharmacist is often responsible for management of the supply of other health products.

Responsibility

Availability and application of pharmaceutical policies, strategies
Internal communication on pharmaceutical policies and strategies
Availability of pharmaceutical operational and management tools
Staff capability in respect to range of pharmacy practice towards patients and other staff
Knowledge of products provided by the pharmacy for use at hospital, and by the patient

Tasks

Ensure the Essential Medicines List is available
Ensure that the Standard Treatment Guidelines are available
Ensure that all essential medicines and medical supplies are at 100% stock level each month
Prescription management tools are available each day
Dispensing staff are available each day in numbers to provide efficient services to the patient
Pharmacy staff are available to the clinical programmes across the hospital
Out-patients are welcomed to the pharmacy to collect their prescriptions
Appropriate advisory services are given to the patient for each medicine or medical supply dispensed
Up to date stock reports for medicines are available each day
Communication on stock status is prepared each day for attention of the Hospital CEO
Stock replenishment is undertaken at a point before the threshold is reached
Patients complaints are addressed by the pharmacist and staff
Pharmacy staff training in communication skills is undertaken annually for all staff

Accountability

Staff are knowledgeable of all pharmaceutical policies, strategies, rules and regulations and policies related to pharmaceutical products, their use, management and logistics
Ensure that strategies and policies have buy-in throughout hospital

Increase pharmaceutical service productivity and quality at the hospital

2. General Communication on Pharmaceutical Services

The hospital pharmacist is responsible and accountable for an efficient communication network on pharmaceutical activities within the hospital and with the patient.

Responsibility

Manage the communication strategies as they apply to pharmacy services at the hospital
Create and implement the Communication plan
Evaluate the effect of the Communication plan at hospital level

Task

Ensure all communication on Pharmacy services at the hospital level is coherent with the hospital and Ministry of Health
Prepare information published about pharmaceutical services at the hospital

Accountability

Accountable for reports and publications or on pharmaceutical services at the hospital
Provide information on pharmaceutical matters related to the hospital

3. Management and procurement of medicines

The hospital pharmacist is responsible and accountable for the preparation of orders from the central medical stores or other approved sources, based on estimates calculated by using the consumption data arising from the health facility. These estimates will include other costs directly or indirectly related to acquisition of medicines, medical supplies and their delivery to the health facility.

Responsibility

Ensure the hospital pharmacy has the relevant tools to collect and process the data on consumption of medicines and medical supplies
Preparing forecasts and quantification for medicines and medical supplies using established programme protocols

Prepare the hospital orders for medicines using the established tools including the established product specifications

Task

Follow the procedures for preparing orders
Collect and process consumption data for essential drugs and medical / surgical supplies on which the orders will be based
Liaise with the central medical stores, district pharmacist during the preparation process

Accountability

Timely and accurate preparation of orders
Comply with MOH processes for ordering of medicines, for data collection and processing, for Consumption data assembly

4. Services to Patients

The hospital pharmacist is responsible and accountable for providing timely pharmaceutical services to patients in order to improve the quality of care.

Responsibility

Ensuring sustained availability of all essential medicines and medical supplies at the hospital at all times
Providing services to the outpatient through dispensing services

Task

Ensure that the hospital has medicines and supplies in quantities estimated for use each month
Ensure dispensary has medicines at all times
Ensure dispensary staff are available at all times during the working hours of the hospital
Ensure that the hospital wards have the required pharmacy staff support and medicines each day
Ensure that the dispensary has dispensing tools to provide service to the patient as well as collect required data
Ensure staff are applying SOPs for dispensing practice

Accountability

Application of correct dispensing practice by pharmacy staff
Availability of all medicines at the store room and at the dispensary
Relevant tools for data collection, processing and transfer
Relevant tools and resources for dispensing and advisory service to the patient

5. Quality Control and Quality Assurance:

The hospital pharmacist is responsible and accountable for accurate implementation of QA programmes in order to ensure that the hospital adheres to safety regulations governing the use of Pharma products and services. Quality control and assurance also applies to medicine and supply safety.

Responsibility

Correct handling and storage of medicines and medical suppliesl
Management of medicines to prevent expiry
Management of pharmaceutical products that fail minimum standards
Provision of correct, quality services to the patient

Task

On a daily basis, ensure that all medicines and medical supplies are kept at the correct storage conditions at the store room, in the dispensary and on the ward
Ensure that the Pharmacy has l Standard Operating Procedures for pharmacy practice in every section of the pharmacy the premises
Ensure that all pharmacy staff are well versed in the SOPs and are applying these in their duty areas
Ensure that patients are provided their medicines in the correct dispensing material (eg, patient packs or dispensing bags)
Apply First Expiry, First Out policy for movement of medicines from the store room to the dispensary, ward and to the patients
Provide on the spot corrective measures to hospital staff who are handling medicines, whenever mistakes are observed
Document all incidents that require corrective measures before referral to hospital CEO
On daily basis, ensure that products about to expire are recorded and notified

to the hospital CEO for appropriate decision and possible re- distribution

Accountability

Availability of Pharmacy SOPs in every section of the pharmacy unit
Application of the SOPs by Pharmacy staff and staff handling medicines at the hospital
Availability of appropriate storage environment for all classes of medicines
Appropriate training material in pharmacy practice at the hospital
Availability of pharmaceutical management tools (policy, SOPs)
Management of drugs to prevent expiry

6. Capacity Building

The hospital pharmacist is responsible and accountable for undertaking regular updates in pharmaceutical service knowledge and skills in applications, in order to provide quality pharmaceutical support services to clinical care and preventative services.

Responsibility

Providing training to pharmacy staff on practice issues
Providing capacity building support to relevant hospital staff
Ensure availability of approved training material

Task

Set up a capacity development programme in specific areas of practice, such as providing dispensing services to the patient
Set up a capacity building programme that uses different approaches (on the job; classroom, etc)
Conduct training to pharmacy staff (including interns) in line with the agreed programme and policy, using the approved tools
Use other trainers as provided by the health sector, to train in technical and practice matters

Accountability

Creating the training programme
Implementation of the training programme
Working with resource or technical assistants

Reporting on the training programme

7. Monitoring, Evaluation & Reporting on Pharmaceutical services at the hospital

Other duties of the pharmacist include monitoring, supervising, evaluating and reporting on pharmaceutical services and its impact at the health facility. Through this function, evidence is gathered that helps inform policy and strategy review and /or formulation.

Responsibility

Carrying out monitoring, evaluation and reporting on pharmaceutical services at the health facility
Participates in developing, standardising and improving monitoring, evaluation and of reporting tools for pharmaceutical services
Participate in pharmacovigilance and post- marketing surveillance services
Analysis of the results and providing reports and recommendation to hospital CEO and other authorities

Task

Collect and process into relevant statistical data against key areas of pharmaceutical service
Prepare report on the pharmaceutical services at the health facility
Provide forecasts on outlook and requirements for pharmaceutical service
Prepare monthly, quarterly and/or bi- annual management report
Monitor the needs for and identify the trends in pharmaceutical services at the health facility level and present reports to CEO

Accountability

Routine monitoring, evaluation and reporting on services using approved framework
Preparation of pharmaceutical service reports
Participation in studies, projects reviewing or improving pharmaceutical services

Table of contents